Number-Challenges

A collection of ingenious number puzzles

Contents

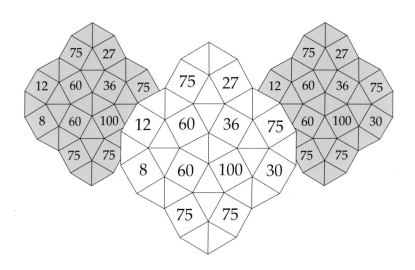

Wilson Ransome

Tarquin Publications

Solve the three challenges opposite
by placing numbers in the cells
so that the rule below always applies.

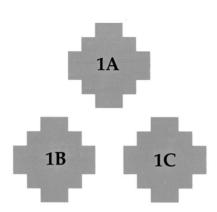

1A

1B   **1C**

The Rule for Group 1

**In every tile of four cells,
the cross-products differ by exactly one.**

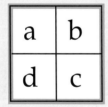

a . c ~ b . d = 1

For example:

5	6
4	5

The cross-products are
5 . 5 = 25, 6 . 4 = 24,
25 - 24 = 1

5	8
2	3

The cross-products are
5 . 3 = 15, 8 . 2 = 16,
16 - 15 = 1

If you would like help, there is a suggested starter tile for each challenge on the centre spread. For a full solution see inside the back cover.

Group 1. A Difference of One

Solve the three challenges opposite
by placing numbers in the cells
so that the rules below always apply.

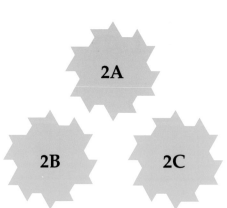

The Rules for Group 2

1
**In every tile of four cells, the number in the
hexagon is the product of the numbers in
the three triangles which surround it.**
2
Use only the listed numbers.

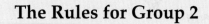

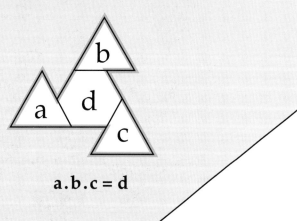

$a.b.c = d$

For example:

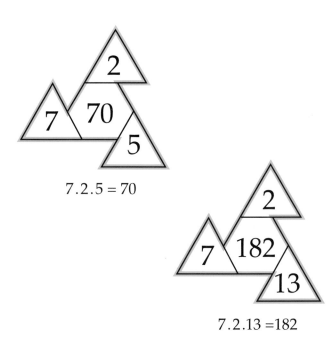

$7.2.5 = 70$

$7.2.13 = 182$

If you would like help, there is a suggested starter tile for each challenge on the centre spread. For a full solution see inside the back cov

Group 2. Twice or Thrice

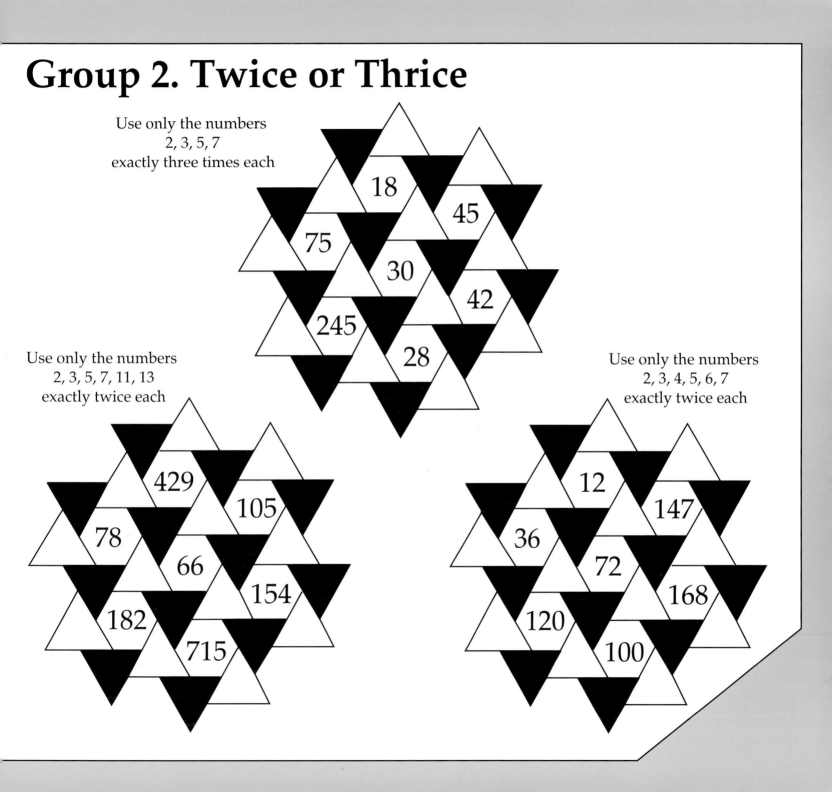

Use only the numbers
2, 3, 5, 7
exactly three times each

18
45
75
30
42
245
28

Use only the numbers
2, 3, 5, 7, 11, 13
exactly twice each

429
105
78
66
154
182
715

Use only the numbers
2, 3, 4, 5, 6, 7
exactly twice each

12
147
36
72
120
168
100

Solve the three challenges opposite
by placing numbers in the cells
so that the rules below always apply.

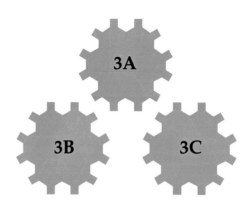

The Rules for Group 3

1

**In every tile of four cells, the number in the
triangle is the product of the numbers in
the three squares which touch it.**

2

Use only the listed numbers.

a.b.c = d

For example:

2.3.2 = 12

5.2.2 = 20

If you would like help, there is a suggested starter tile for each challenge on the centre spread. For a full solution see inside the back cove

Group 3. Three-factor Products

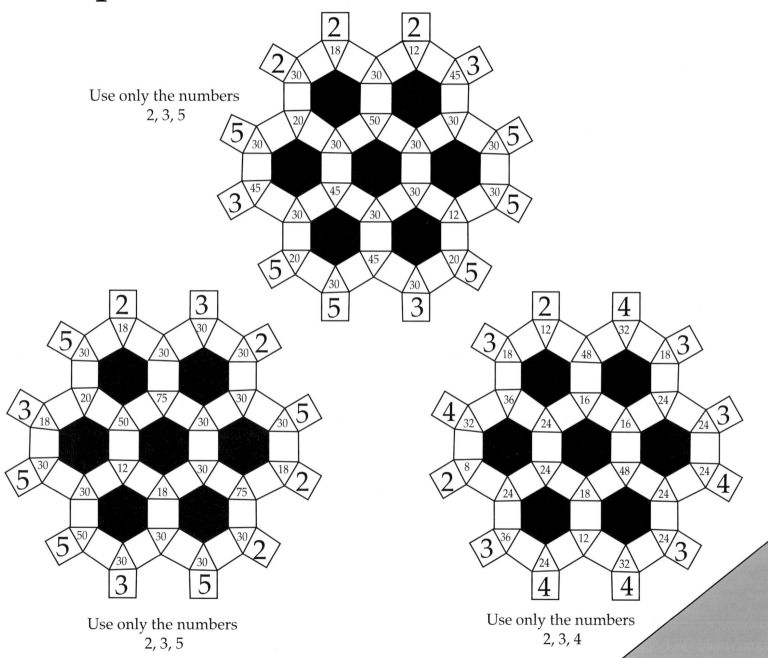

Use only the numbers
2, 3, 5

Use only the numbers
2, 3, 5

Use only the numbers
2, 3, 4

Solve the three challenges opposite
by placing numbers in the cells
so that the rules below always apply.

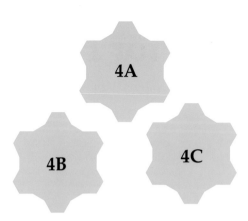

4A

4B

4C

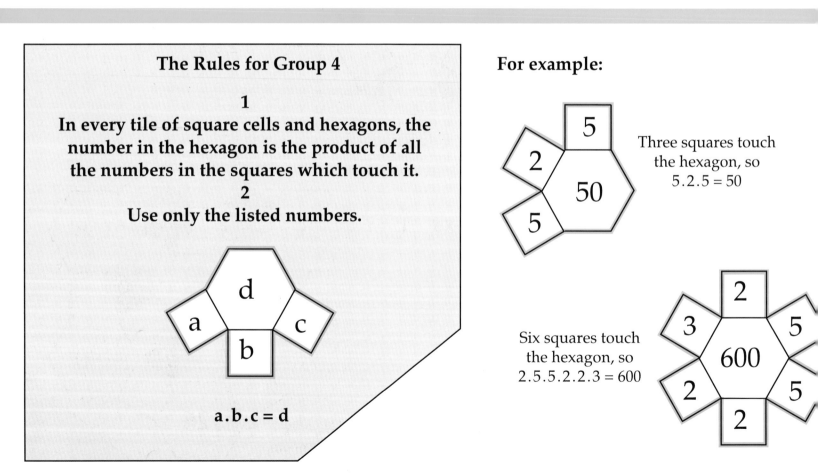

The Rules for Group 4

1

In every tile of square cells and hexagons, the number in the hexagon is the product of all the numbers in the squares which touch it.

2

Use only the listed numbers.

a.b.c = d

For example:

5

2

50

5

Three squares touch
the hexagon, so
5.2.5 = 50

2

3

5

600

2

5

2

Six squares touch
the hexagon, so
2.5.5.2.2.3 = 600

If you would like help, there is a suggested starter tile for each challenge on the centre spread. For a full solution see inside the back cov

Group 4. Products by Touching

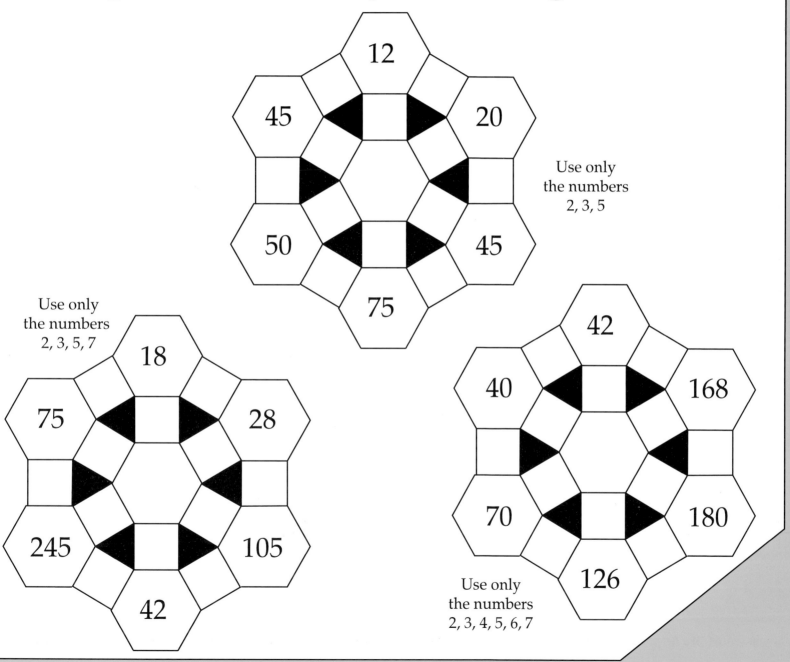

Use only the numbers 2, 3, 5

Use only the numbers 2, 3, 5, 7

Use only the numbers 2, 3, 4, 5, 6, 7

Solve the three challenges opposite
by placing numbers in the cells
so that the rules below always apply.

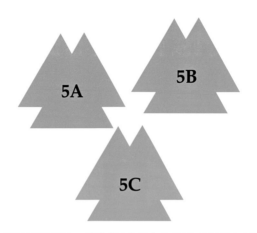

The Rules for Group 5

1

**In every triangular tile of four cells, the number
in the hexagon is the product of the three numbers
in the triangles which surround it.**

2

Use only the listed numbers.

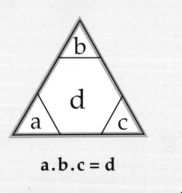

a.b.c = d

For example:

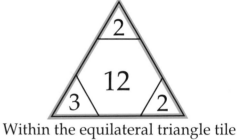

Within the equilateral triangle tile
$3.2.2 = 12$

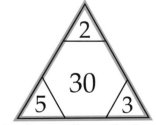

Within the equilateral triangle tile
$5.2.3 = 30$

If you would like help, there is a suggested starter tile for each challenge on the centre spread. For a full solution see inside the back cover

Group 5. Factor Surround

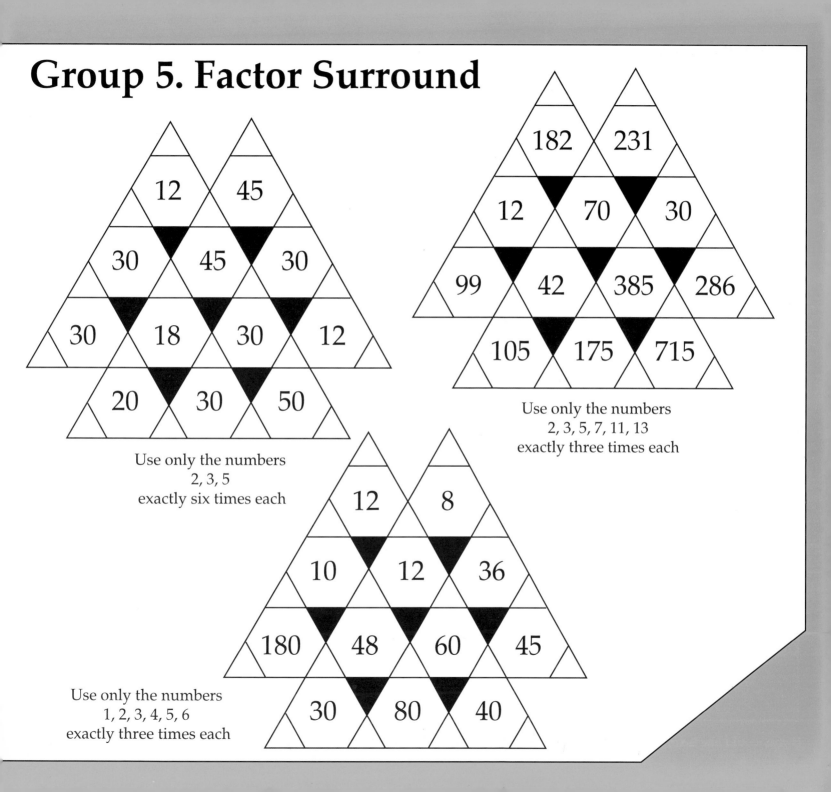

Use only the numbers
2, 3, 5
exactly six times each

Use only the numbers
2, 3, 5, 7, 11, 13
exactly three times each

Use only the numbers
1, 2, 3, 4, 5, 6
exactly three times each

Solve the three challenges opposite
by placing numbers in the cells
so that the rules below always apply.

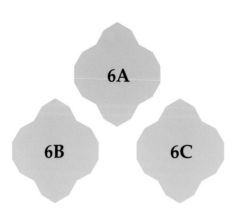

6A

6B

6C

The Rule for Group 6

For example:

1

In every tile of square cells and triangles, the number in the square is the product of all the numbers in the triangles which touch it.

2

Any number in a triangle is prime.

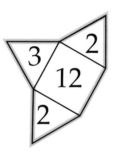

Three triangles
touch the square, so
3.2.2 = 12

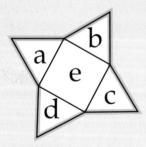

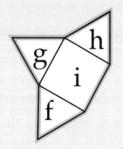

a.b.c.d = e   f.g.h = i

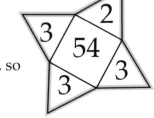

Four triangles
touch the square, so
3.2.3.3 = 54

If you would like help, there is a suggested starter tile for each challenge on the centre spread. For a full solution see inside the back cover

Group 6. Always Prime

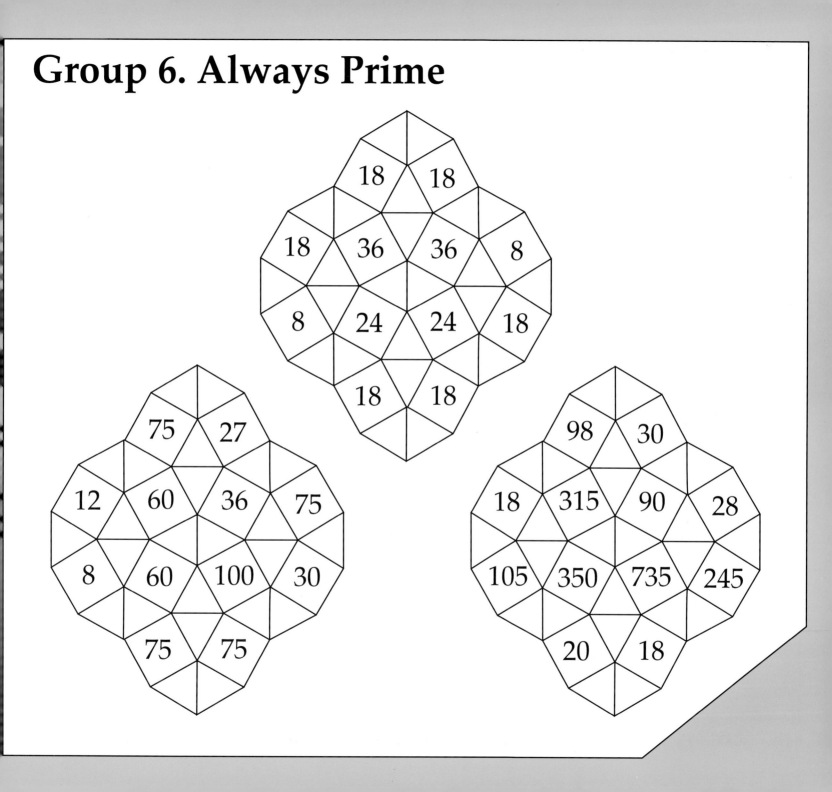

Solve the three challenges opposite
by placing numbers in the cells
so that the rules below always apply.

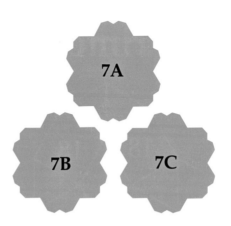

The Rules for Group 7

1

In every tile of five cells, the number in the square is the product of the numbers in the four pentagons which surround it.

2

Use only the listed numbers.

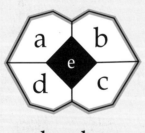

a.b.c.d = e

For example:

7.2.5.7 = 490

5.2.3.11 = 330

If you would like help, there is a suggested starter tile for each challenge on the centre spread. For a full solution see inside the back cover

Group 7. Four-factor Products

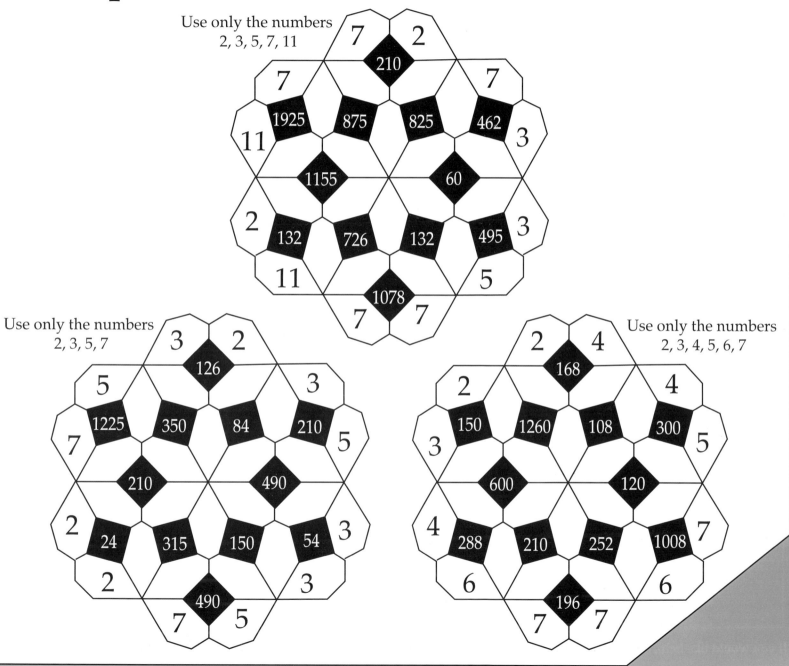

Use only the numbers
2, 3, 5, 7, 11

Use only the numbers
2, 3, 5, 7

Use only the numbers
2, 3, 4, 5, 6, 7

Solve the three challenges opposite
by placing numbers in the cells
so that the rules below always apply.

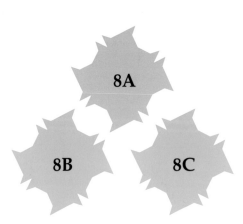

The Rules for Group 8

1

**In every tile of five cells, the difference
between the cross-products is the number
in the centre square.**

2

Only single digit numbers are allowed.

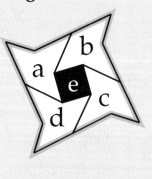

a.c ~ b.d = e

For example:

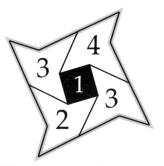

The cross-products are
3.3 = 9, 4.2 = 8,
9 - 8 = 1

The cross-products are
6.9 = 54, 8.7 = 56,
56 - 54 = 2

If you would like help, there is a suggested starter tile for each challenge on the centre spread. For a full solution see inside the back cover

Group 8. Single Digit Differences

Starter Tiles

Use these diagrams if you would like some help with a particular challenge whilst avoiding looking at the full solutions.

For some challenges, it is very important to start at the suggested tile. For others it is just one among several possible starting points.

Group 1. A Difference of One

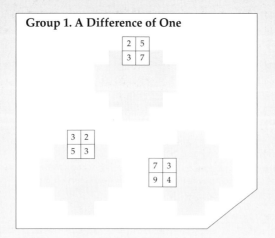

Group 2. Twice or Thrice

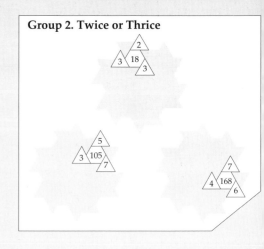

Group 3. Three-factor Products

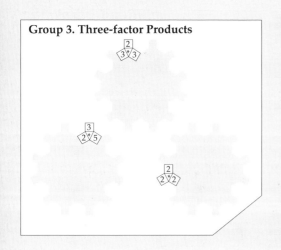

Group 4. Products by Touching

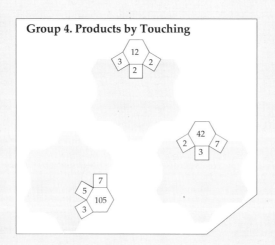

Group 5. Factor Surround

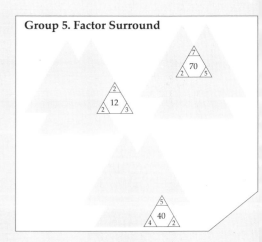

Group 6. Always Prime

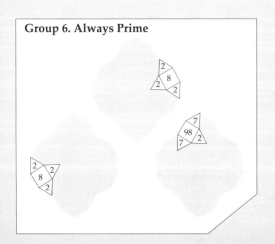

Group 7. Four-factor Products

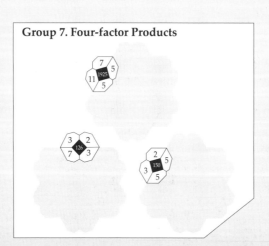

Group 8. Single Digit Differences

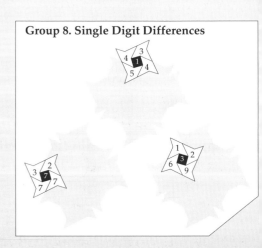

Group 9. Adding Towards the Centre

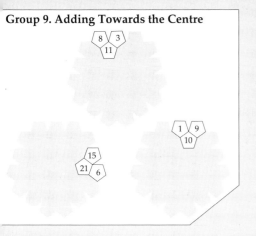

Group 10. Consecutive Roundabout

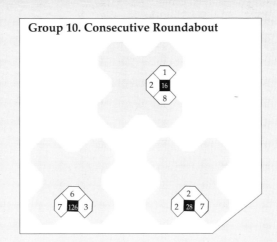

Group 11. Consecutive Square-about

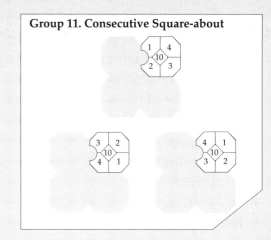

Group 12. Sum to the Stars

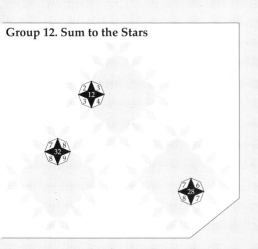

Group 13. Tables Tiles

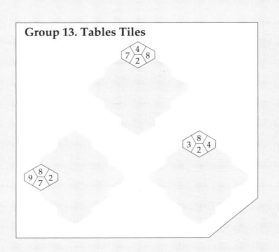

Group 14. Sequence Sums

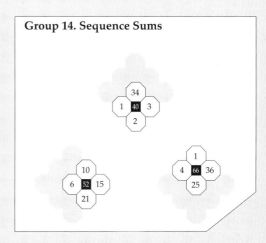

Group 15. More Sequence Sums

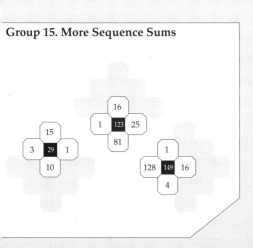

Group 16. Multiplying Around the Centre

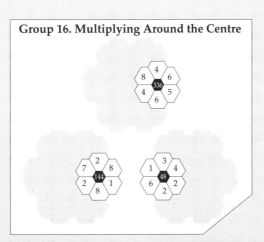

Solve the three challenges opposite
by placing numbers in the cells
so that the rules below always apply.

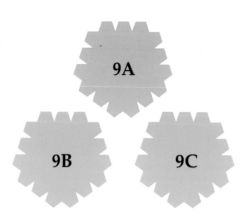

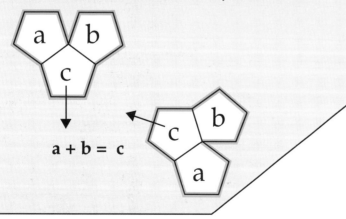

The Rules for Group 9

1
In every tile of three cells in this arrangement,
the number in the pentagon nearest the centre
of the pattern is the sum of the other two.

2
The outermost ring of pentagons contains all
the numbers from 1 to 15, once each.

a + b = c

For example:

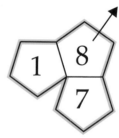

The 8 is nearest
the centre and so
1 + 7 = 8

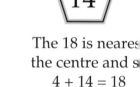

The 18 is neares
the centre and s
4 + 14 = 18

There are twenty different
routes leading towards the centre,
and another rule when you get there:

If you would like help, there is a suggested starter tile for each challenge on the centre spread. For a full solution see inside the back cove

Group 9. Adding Towards the Centre

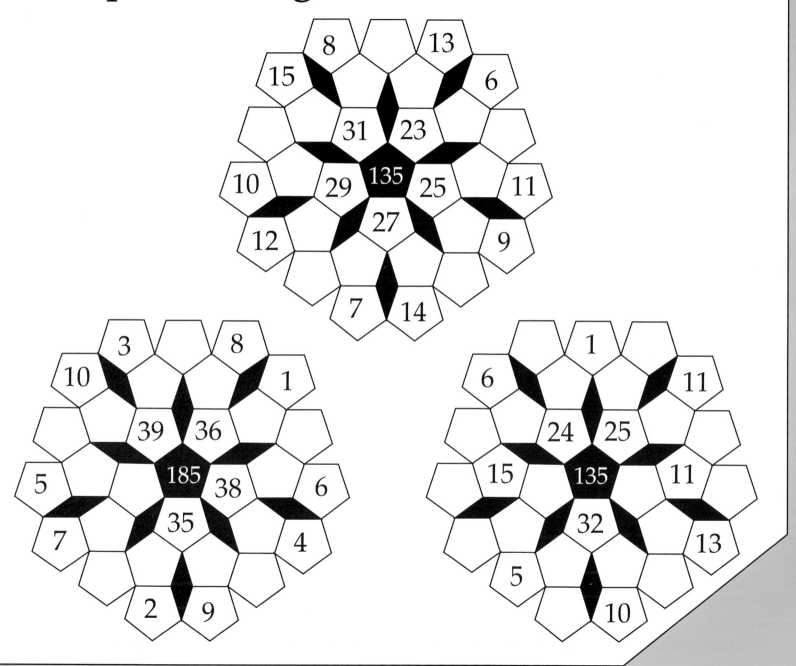

Solve the three challenges opposite
by placing numbers in the cells
so that the rules below always apply.

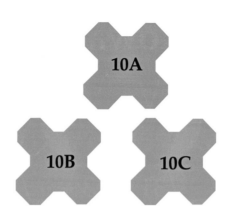

The Rules for Group 10

1

**In every tile of five cells with a circle
at the centre, the number in the circle
is the sum of four consecutive numbers
in the surrounding cells.
They may be written clockwise or anticlockwise.**

2

**The product of the three numbers surrounding
each square must be the number in the square.**

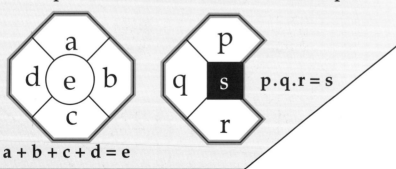

$$a + b + c + d = e$$

$$p.q.r = s$$

For example:

With a circle at the centre, the
numbers must be consecutive and
the sum must be calculated.

$$3 + 4 + 5 + 6 = 18$$

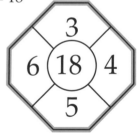

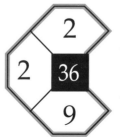

With a square at the centre,
the product must be calculated.

$$2.2.9 = 36$$

If you would like help, there is a suggested starter tile for each challenge on the centre spread. For a full solution see inside the back cover.

Group 10. Consecutive Roundabout

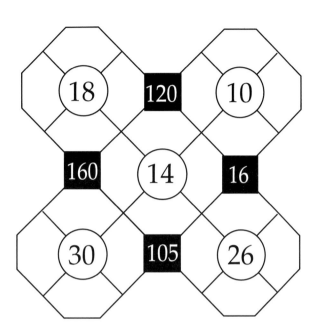

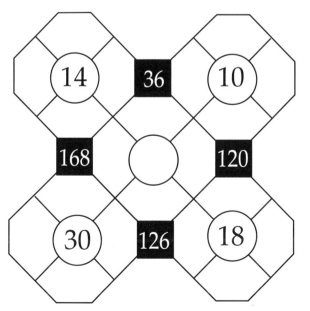

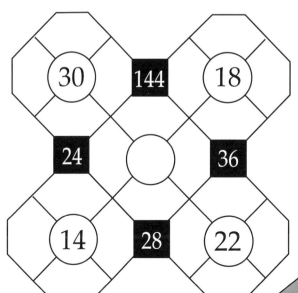

Solve the three challenges opposite
by placing numbers in the cells
so that the rules below always apply.

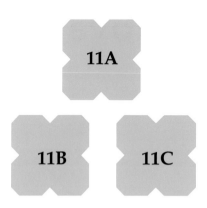

11A

11B   **11C**

The Rules for Group 11

1

**In every tile of five cells with a square
at the centre, the number in the centre square
is the sum of four consecutive numbers
in the surrounding cells.
They may be written clockwise or anticlockwise.**

2

**The product of the four numbers surrounding
each circle must be the number in the circle.**

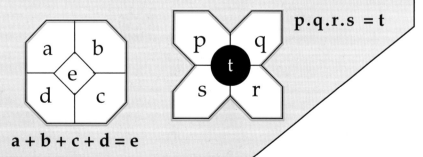

$$p.q.r.s = t$$

$$a + b + c + d = e$$

For example:

With a square at the centre, the
numbers must be consecutive and
the sum must be calculated.
$7 + 8 + 9 + 10 = 34$

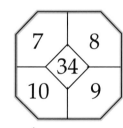

With a circle at the centre,
the product must be calculated.
$4.6.3.1 = 72$

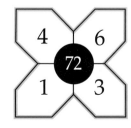

If you would like help, there is a suggested starter tile for each challenge on the centre spread. For a full solution see inside the back cover

Group 11. Consecutive Square-about

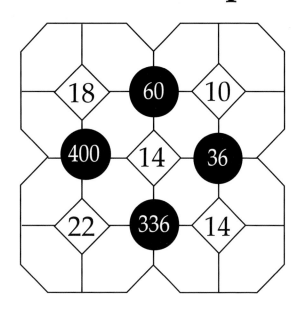

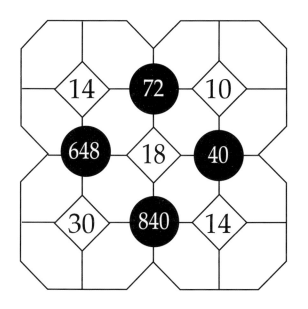

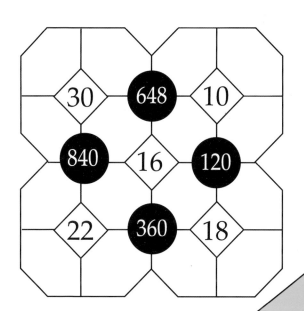

Solve the three challenges opposite
by placing numbers in the cells
so that the rules below always apply.

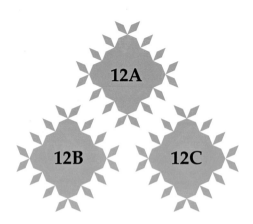

The Rules for Group 12

1

**In every tile of five cells with a black star
at the centre, the number in the star is the sum of
the four numbers in the surrounding cells.**

2

**The four numbers around a point are consecutive.
They may be written clockwise or anticlockwise.**

$a + b + c + d = e$

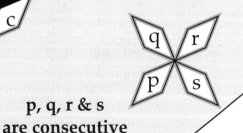

**p, q, r & s
are consecutive**

For example:

The numbers in the four outer cells
add up to the number in the black star.
$7 + 6 + 3 + 4 = 20$

These numbers around each point
are consecutive.

If you would like help, there is a suggested starter tile for each challenge on the centre spread. For a full solution see inside the back cove

Group 12. Sum to the Stars

Solve the three challenges opposite
by placing numbers in the cells
so that the rules below always apply.

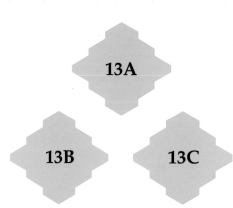

13A

13B   **13C**

The Rules for Group 13

1

**In every tile of four cells, there is a simple
multiplication sum and also the two digit result.**

2

**In the vertical tiles the digits read clockwise,
in the horizontal tiles they read anti-clockwise.**

There are four possibilities:

$a.b = 10c + d$
$b.c = 10d + a$
$c.d = 10a + b$
$d.a = 10b + c$

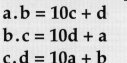

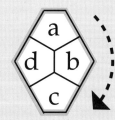

For example:

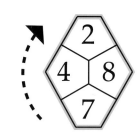

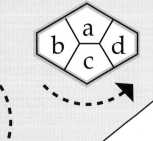

Starting with the digit 7
in each kind of tile
$7.4 = 28$

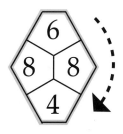

Starting with the digit 6
in each kind of tile
$6.8 = 48$

If you would like help, there is a suggested starter tile for each challenge on the centre spread. For a full solution see inside the back cover.

Group 13. Tables Tiles

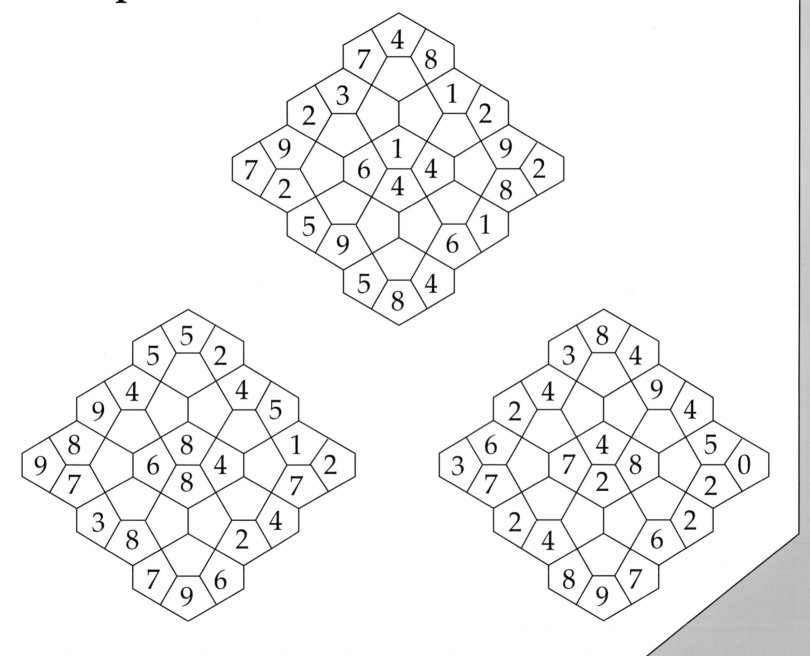

Solve the three challenges opposite
by placing numbers in the cells
so that the rules below always apply.

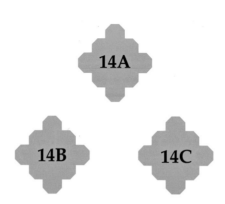

14A

14B   **14C**

The Rules for Group 14

1
**In every tile of five cells, the number
in the centre square is always the sum of
the numbers in the four surrounding cells.**
2
**Use only numbers which are listed in the
given sequences, once each.**

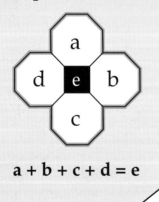

a + b + c + d = e

For example:

From the sequence of
Fibonacci numbers

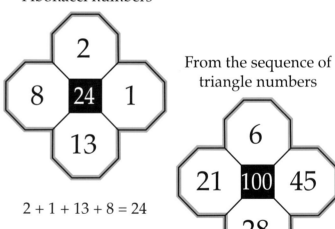

From the sequence of
triangle numbers

2 + 1 + 13 + 8 = 24

6 + 45 + 28 + 21 = 100

If you would like help, there is a suggested starter tile for each challenge on the centre spread. For a full solution see inside the back cover.

Group 14. Sequence Sums

Use only numbers from this sequence
of Fibonacci numbers:
1, 1, 2, 3, 5, 8, 13, 21, 34

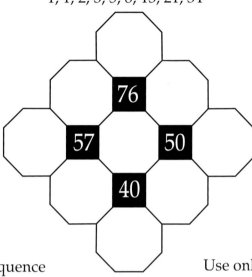

Use only numbers from this sequence
of triangle numbers:
1, 3, 6, 10, 15, 21, 28, 36, 45

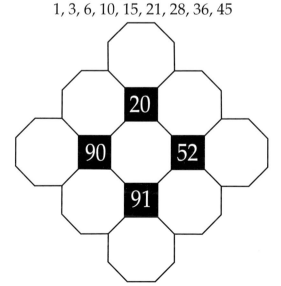

Use only numbers from this sequence
of square numbers:
1, 4, 9, 16, 25, 36, 49, 64, 81

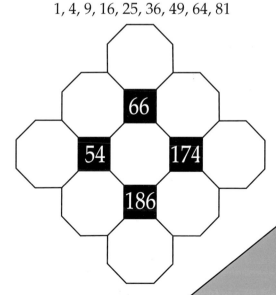

Solve the three challenges opposite
by placing numbers in the cells
so that the rules below always apply.

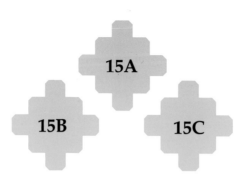

15A

15B   **15C**

The Rules for Group 15

1
**In every tile of five cells, the number
in the centre square is always the sum of
the numbers in the four surrounding cells.**

2
**Use only numbers which are listed in the
given sequences, once each.**

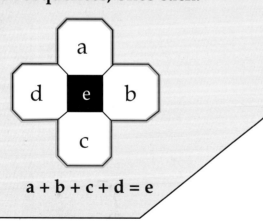

a + b + c + d = e

For example:

From the sequence of
square numbers

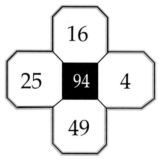

16 + 4 + 49 + 25 = 94

From the sequence of
powers of two numbers

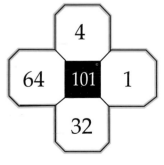

4 + 1 + 32 + 64 = 101

If you would like help, there is a suggested starter tile for each challenge on the centre spread. For a full solution see inside the back cover.

Group 15. More Sequence Sums

Use only numbers from this sequence
of square numbers:
1, 4, 9, 16, 25, 36, 49, 64, 81

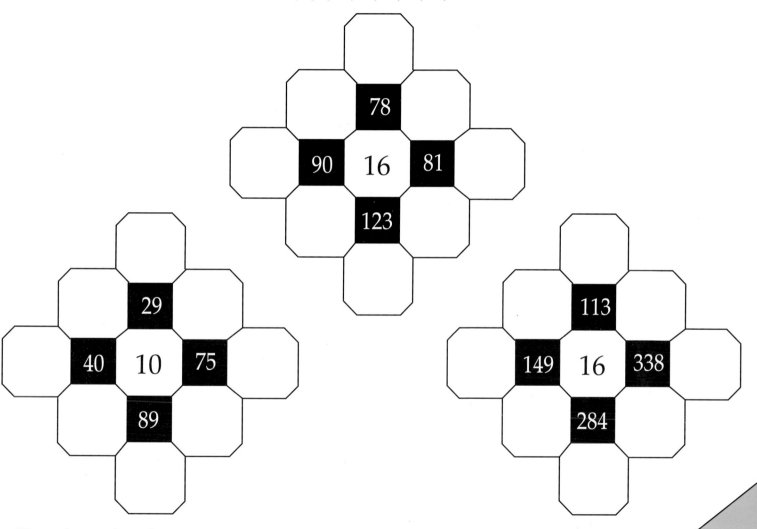

Use only numbers from this sequence
of triangle numbers:
1, 3, 6, 10, 15, 21, 28, 36, 45

Use only numbers from this sequence of
numbers which are powers of two:
1, 2, 4, 8, 16, 32, 64, 128, 256

Solve the three challenges opposite by placing numbers in the cells so that the rules below always apply.

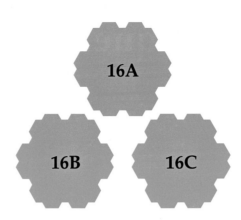

16A

16B

16C

The Rules for Group 16

In every tile of seven cells, the number in the hexagon is the result of two different multiplication sums.
For one, start at the top and multiply that digit by the two digit number following. Then start at the bottom and continue on round in the same way.
You can go round the hexagon in either a clockwise or anticlockwise direction.

Either clockwise
$$a.(10b + c) = g$$
$$\& \ d.(10e + f) = g$$
or anticlockwise
$$a.(10f + e) = g$$
$$\& \ d.(10c + b) = g$$

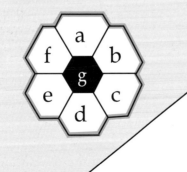

For example:

In this tile, the numbers read clockwise
$$8.15 = 120$$
$$\& \ 5.24 = 120$$

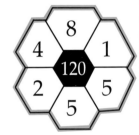

In this tile, the numbers read anticlockwise
$$7.36 = 252$$
$$\& \ 9.28 = 252$$

If you would like help, there is a suggested starter tile for each challenge on the centre spread. For a full solution see inside the back cover.

Group 16. Multiplying Around the Centre

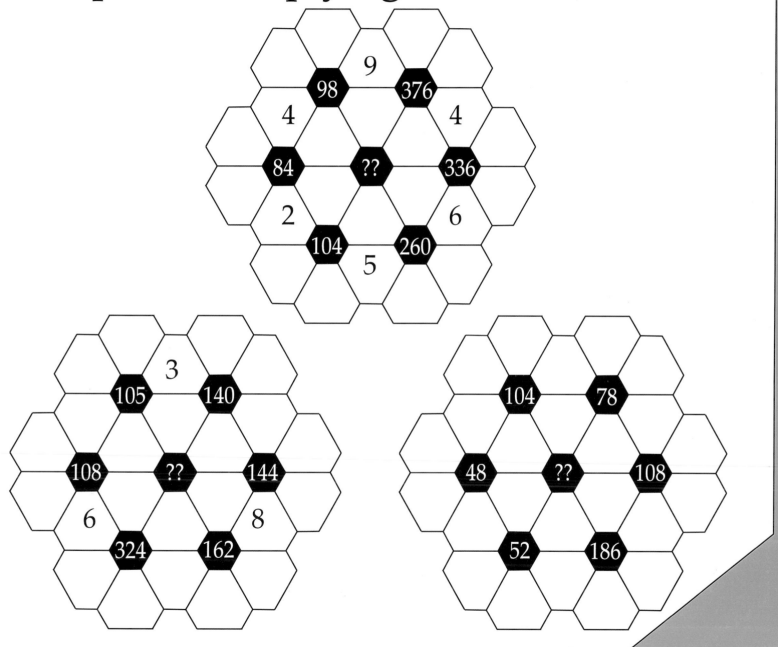

Solutions

Here are the full solutions.

If all you need is a little help to get you started, look at the centre spread for the starter tiles.

Group 1. A Difference of One

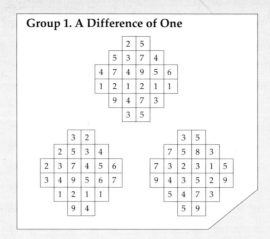

Group 2. Twice or Thrice

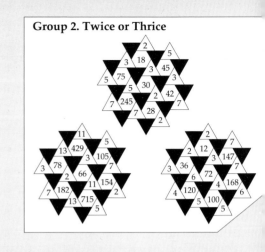

Group 3. Three-factor Products

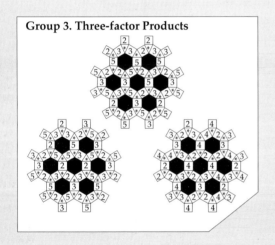

Group 4. Products by Touching

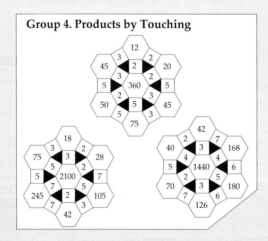

Group 5. Factor Surround

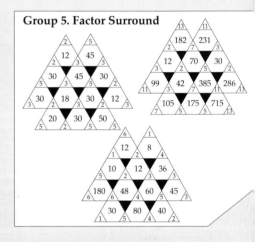

Group 6. Always Prime

Group 7. Four-factor Products

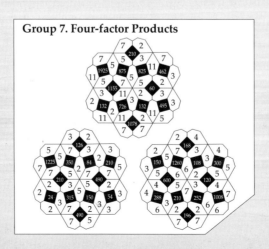

Group 8. Single Digit Differences

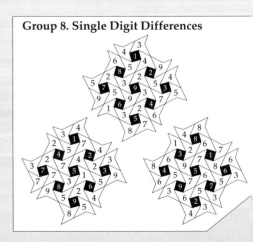